ADVENTURES WITH THE GODS

By CATHARINE F. SELLEW

ADVENTURES *with the* GODS
ADVENTURES *with the* GIANTS
ADVENTURES *with the* HEROES

ADVENTURES WITH THE GODS

CATHARINE F. SELLEW

WITH ILLUSTRATIONS BY GEORGE AND DORIS HAUMAN

LITTLE, BROWN AND COMPANY · BOSTON

Twenty-fifth Printing

TO
KAKIE

Preface

THESE STORIES that I have written are not really my stories. They are much older than I am. They are much older than your mother and father, or your grandmother and grandfather, or your grandfather's grandfather. They are so old that they were told thousands of years before Christopher Columbus discovered America!

There weren't any books in those long-ago days. And in the ancient land of Greece the only stories people knew were told to them by men who went from town to town singing of brave heroes, beautiful maidens and terrible dragons. These men came to great feasts and sang to the guests about all the things they had seen and heard in strange lands.

The people wondered about the strange and interesting things in the sky and on the earth. How were such things made? They wondered why the plants and animals lived, and grew, and died. They didn't think of God as we do, as one God of the whole world. But they had great skill in telling beautiful stories about what they thought had happened. So the singers at the feasts sang these stories of powerful gods and goddesses who, they believed, made and ruled the earth. They sang of how these gods and goddesses helped as well as punished the people on the earth.

The stories in this book are some of the songs that were sung at those feasts. Today we call them "myths." Some of the names of the men and women in the myths, and the places where they lived, may be hard to say out loud; but if you look at the last pages of this book, you will find a list of the names in the order of the alphabet. It will show you how to say them.

Contents

ADVENTURES WITH THE GODS

Prometheus and the Fire

MANY, MANY hundreds of years ago there was a mountain in a country we now call Greece. The mountain's name was Olympus. This mountain was so high that it reached way up into the sky even beyond the clouds. Sometimes it would put on one of the clouds for a cap, and sometimes it would use one of the softest clouds for a muffler.

On top of this Mount Olympus there was a beautiful city surrounded by a gate of thick clouds, guarded by the Hours and Seasons. This city was always full of sunshine and in it there were beautiful palaces built all of marble.

The people who lived in this city were very great and powerful. They were so much more powerful than either you or I that they could make it rain or shine just as they pleased. They could make the people on the earth, far, far below, do anything they wished. They could make rivers run and flowers bloom. Because of this they were called gods and goddesses.

Jupiter was the king of the gods, and when he was angry he made it rain very hard and hurled great thunderbolts down on to the earth, and the lightning would flash about him. All the people down below on the earth would hide, and even the gods and goddesses would be afraid. For you see they had feelings just like us. They walked and talked and did the same things we do, but they also could do many things that we can't do.

Jupiter had a court full of many wonderful people. The god of the sun and the goddess of the moon were his children. His wife was Juno, the queen of the gods. She was beautiful but very jealous.

There was one god in Jupiter's court who was very brave, and wasn't afraid of the king. His name was Prometheus. Prometheus was interested in the land far below, and one day he made some human beings out of earth and water to live there. He used to watch the boys and girls playing in the bright sunshine with the squirrels and chipmunks, and he grew to love them.

4

When autumn came and the cold winds began to blow, he watched the children shivering, and saw that they weren't laughing the way they used to in the summertime. The animals, their playmates, ran into their holes but the people of the earth didn't have any holes big enough and warm enough for them. Prometheus was very sorry about this.

Up on high Olympus where he lived they never had any winter weather. He wondered if he couldn't bring the people of earth up there to visit him, but no human beings were allowed on Mount Olympus. There were so many men and women and children that he knew he would never be able to hide them even in the soft fluffy clouds. Prometheus thought and thought.

Suddenly he remembered Vulcan, who was the blacksmith of the gods. Vulcan had a great anvil in his workshop deep down under the earth. Sometimes in the middle of the night you can hear strange rumblings; that is when Vulcan and his helpers are forging swords and shields for the gods. Prometheus knew that, to make these things, Vulcan had to have fire.

If he could get some of that fire and give it to the humans, they would be able to keep warm, and cook hot soup and good things to eat! Of course he would have to teach them how to use fire, so that they wouldn't burn their fingers.

The eyes of Prometheus sparkled with excitement when he thought of this way to help his friends of the earth, and he began to prepare for his journey. It was a long way and Prometheus didn't want Jupiter, the great king, to know where he was going. So one night, after dressing warmly, for it was very cold on the way down to Vulcan's workshop, he started down the Milky Way to Earth.

When Prometheus finally reached the earth, he went to a great cave near the ocean. In that cave was a long flight of narrow stone steps that were slippery with moss. Little black animals scuttled out of his way as Prometheus started down the dark stairs. The air smelled of wet earth and drops of water trickled down the sides of the rocks. He went down, down, down, and it got blacker and blacker — for Prometheus was miles and miles under the earth.

Suddenly he saw a warm glow at the bottom of the steps. It came from a crack under a heavy oak door. From inside there came the sound of clashing and ringing metal. The young god knocked loudly on the door.

"Who's there?" a deep voice roared.

"Prometheus."

"Hello! What brings you here?" the voice exclaimed, and Prometheus could hear a bolt slide back and the great door swung open. The brilliant light from the forges blinded him for a minute; then he saw a huge hunchbacked figure standing in front of him. It was the god Vulcan.

"Come in! Come in!" Vulcan said. "What can I do for you? You have come a long way!"

Prometheus explained that he had just come for a visit. It had been a long time since he had seen the blacksmith. He knew that Vulcan was not allowed to give away the fire of the gods, but he told him about the people on earth who were so cold.

"Well now, that's too bad," Vulcan said sympathetically. "However, I'm afraid there's not much we can do about it, is there?" But he winked as he said it, and went on with his work, leaving Prometheus to look around the shop.

While Vulcan was very busy hammering out the red-hot blade of a great sword, Prometheus lit a torch from one of the forges, silently unbolted the heavy oak door, and ran quickly back up the long flight of stone steps.

That very morning all the children of the earth crowded around Prometheus to see the bright thing he held in his hand.

"That's fire," Prometheus explained. One of the children reached up to touch the flame. "Don't put your hand in the flame," the god warned. "It will hurt you! *This* is what you must do with it." And Prometheus showed them how to gather twigs and sticks and put them in a pile. Then he touched one of the twigs with the flame and started the bonfire. It was nice and warm around the fire. Soon the people of the earth were laughing and happy, and they thanked the god Prometheus again and again. Prometheus was happy too, because he had been able to help his friends.

Prometheus Bound

WHEN JUPITER saw how healthy and happy the people on the earth were even in the coldest kind of winter weather, he began to wonder. He did not want them to be too powerful for he was afraid they would try to conquer Mount Olympus and take his kingdom from him. He was very angry with Prometheus for making such fine strong human beings.

So one day he disguised himself as an old man with a long beard and a cane, and went down to play with the children. He soon discovered how clever they were, and saw that they were using the fire of the gods to keep them warm.

Fire was not meant for human hands. The great Jupiter was very angry! The sky became black with heavy thunderclouds, and the earth trembled with the fear of what might come.

"Who gave fire to the earth?" thundered the great king, forgetting that he was disguised.

Everyone was frightened when such a fierce voice came out of this kindly old man. They ran very fast and hid in caves and up high in the trees, and all the little animals scuttled into their holes.

"Answer me!" roared the god. But everyone was too frightened to answer. Even the gods on high Olympus trembled with fear as they looked down on the earth.

"Then I'll find out for myself!" he cried. "You forget I am the great Jupiter!" And he went to the very cave that Prometheus had gone to, and leaped down the stairs four steps at a time. With one blow of his fist he broke down the heavy oak door and burst into Vulcan's workshop.

"Did you give those people fire?" demanded the great king. Vulcan, the blacksmith, knew it was Prometheus who had taken the fire, but he did not want to tell because he, too, had felt sorry for them. He thought he would try to soften Jupiter's anger.

"No, but come and see the shield I am making you. It is the strongest and most beautiful shield I have ever made."

Jupiter looked neither to the right nor to the left.

"*Who gave those people the fire of the gods?*" he insisted. "I demand an answer." When the great king talked like this, the other gods did not dare to tell a lie, for they knew he would find out the truth.

"Prometheus," Vulcan replied, and his head was bent very low — for he loved Prometheus.

"He will suffer for this! He had no right to take that fire! Listen to me and do as I say," commanded the great Jupiter. "You must make the strongest possible chains, and tie Prometheus to a great rock at the end of the world. I will send one of my eagles to torture him night and day, but never kill him." With this terrible threat, Jupiter strode back to his throne on high Olympus.

Vulcan was very unhappy, but he had to carry out the king's commands. All the other gods and goddesses were sorry for Prometheus, too, but there was nothing they could do.

The hunchbacked blacksmith sadly hammered the heavy rings of the chains he was forced to make for his friend Prometheus.

When they were finished, he dragged them slowly up the dark steps to earth. They rattled and rang on the cold stones.

Prometheus waited near a great rock that stood black against the sky. He had been brought there by Jupiter's servants. Around and around the rock flew an eagle with evil black eyes and a big curved beak. He was waiting for Vulcan to chain Prometheus.

Vulcan tied the chains around the god's wrists and ankles. Then he drove the hooks at the end of the chains into the rock itself. Now Prometheus could not move. Vulcan hated to leave him so helpless and unable to protect himself against the fierce eagle.

But Prometheus was very brave, and he knew a terribly important secret. He knew that someday a great hero would free him from his bonds, and he was willing to wait for that hero to come. He was so wise that people from far and wide came to the rock where he was bound and asked for advice. Prometheus knew that his punishment would not hurt his friends, the people of the earth, and he was glad of that.

Mercury Steals Apollo's Cattle

ONE DAY a very long time ago, even before Prometheus was chained to the rock at the end of the world, the god of the sun, Phoebus Apollo, peeked up over the edge of the ocean. He shot one of his golden beams into the open mouth of a large, dark cave. The sunbeam fell on a newborn baby.

The baby laughed and kicked his heels joyfully in the air. He tried to catch the bright, pretty thing with his tiny hands. But the sun did not know yet that this baby was his new brother, Mercury, who would one day be messenger of the gods. For Mercury's father was none other than the great Jupiter. And his mother was Maia, a beautiful nymph who lived by the sea.

Phoebus Apollo soon lost interest. He left the cave, and rose high up in the sky — too far away to watch this wonder child.

Young Mercury sat up in his cradle and

looked around. Where had that pretty golden beam gone? But his mother was sleeping on her bed, and the cave was dark and cool again. Outside he could hear the waves washing up on the shore. He could hear the sea gulls' harsh cries. It looked bright and beautiful out there to Mercury.

Looking again at his mother, and sure that she was sound asleep, the baby climbed out of his cradle and tiptoed to the entrance of the cave. You must remember Mercury was not an ordinary baby. He was the youngest son of the great Jupiter, and he already had many godlike powers.

The sunlight was so bright after the darkness of the cave that Mercury had to blink and put his hand up to his eyes. But the air was warm and smelled of the salt of the sea. Mercury laughed with delight. It was a wonderful world!

A foamy wave slipped into the cave and ran around the moss-covered rocks, and then slipped out again. The water felt cold to Mercury's toes, and he jumped to safety on a bigger brown rock.

Suddenly the brown rock began to move! It moved very slowly, but Mercury was so surprised that he was just a little bit afraid. He tried to hold on tight, but it was hard on such a smooth, round surface. Up and down! Bumpety-bump! And then a head with two black, beady eyes came out from under the brown rock. But it wasn't a rock at all. It was a big turtle!

"Get off my back!" said the turtle in a very nasty tone of voice.

"I didn't know you were a turtle," replied Mercury. And he laughed and laughed.

"Get off my back," the turtle repeated. He didn't even say "Please." "I don't like little boys riding on my back. In fact I don't like little boys at all!" The turtle was an ugly turtle.

Then Mercury had an idea. It was an idea that only a very unusual baby would think of. The turtle's shell was pretty, and it made a nice sound when he tapped on it. First he killed the old turtle, and took the shell from its back. Then he tiptoed into the cave and pulled nine linen threads from the sheet in his cradle. He tied these threads tightly across the turtle's shell, and when he touched them with his fingers they made music. It was sweet and gay, and Mercury danced with delight out of the cave and into the sunshine. He had made a kind of small harp called a lyre.

The sand along the seashore was smooth and white, and packed down hard by the pounding of the waves. Mercury ran and danced and jumped along the beach. When he looked behind him, he saw that his footprints made patterns in the sand. What fun it was!

For a long time Mercury played along the beach, going farther and farther away from his mother and the cave. After a while he came to a beautiful mountain. Its sides sloped down to the sea, and it was covered with large trees and smooth grassy fields. Mercury was getting tired of the seashore. He decided to climb the mountain. It was getting late. Phoebus Apollo looked like a fiery red ball dropping down behind the mountain. But on the other side, the silvery white moon goddess, Diana, was sailing up into the sky. She gave plenty of light for this child, Mercury, who already could do things like a man.

Up and up the mountain he climbed, all the time singing a gay little song. Finally he came to a field. There, eating the sweet grass, was a great herd of cattle. There were oxen and cows, and they were much, much bigger than the oxen and cows that you and I see on the farms in the country. Their smooth, glossy sides shone in the moonlight. Mercury knew that they were the cattle of his brother, Phoebus Apollo, god of the sun! But, strangely enough, there wasn't anyone around to watch them.

"How very careless of my brother," said Mercury. "He should know better than to leave his beautiful cattle unguarded." And Mercury smiled to himself. What a good joke it would be to drive the cattle out of the field and hide them. But Apollo would see their hoof prints and follow. Mercury hadn't forgotten how his footprints had made patterns in the sand on the seashore.

Mercury sat down on the ground and looked at the cattle. He thought for a few minutes. Suddenly he jumped up and began to gather some twigs. He tied them together in two bunches, and then fastened one on each foot.

"Now Apollo will never recognize my footprints," laughed Mercury. But the cattle . . . What was he going to do about the cattle's hoofprints? Mercury sat down again and thought some more.

"I know," he finally said to himself. "I'll make them walk backwards!" Then Mercury broke a long branch from a bush in the field, and drove the cattle backwards across wide fields and down the steep mountain.

On the way they passed an old man. The old man was mending his fishing nets, and he stopped in surprise. Never had he seen such a sight in his life! Who was this baby driving a great herd of cattle *backwards?*

"Good evening," cried Mercury gaily. The old man only stared at him in wonder.

"You look like a wise old man," said Mercury. The old man shook his head in a frightened way. "If you are," continued the young god, "don't tell anyone that you saw me. The gods might be angry."

The old man nodded again, still unable to speak. He could not believe what he saw and heard.

Soon Mercury came to a valley into which there led only a narrow path. The steep mountains hid it from the sea on one side, and from near-by fields on the other. Here Apollo would not think to look for his cattle. Mercury laughed with glee. But he knew that his brother would be very angry. If he ever discovered that it was Mercury who had stolen them, he would punish him. Only their father, the great Jupiter, could protect Mercury from Apollo's anger.

Mercury did not think Apollo would miss just two of his great herd, and he thought that a sacrifice of such beautiful cattle would please his father very much. It was the custom in those days for people who were in trouble to make what they called a "sacrifice" to the gods on high Olympus in order to win their help. This meant burning something they liked very much on an altar. So Mercury killed two of Apollo's cattle and burned them in honor of Jupiter.

When he had finished the sacrifice, he kicked the ashes over the ground so there would be no trace of the fire, or of what he had done. He was tired and sleepy after all this. So he left the cattle to graze in the hidden valley, and ran back in the bright moonlight to his mother in her cave by the sea.

The next morning Apollo, great god of the sun, left his chariot standing way up in the sky, and came down to earth to see his beautiful cattle. But, lo and behold, there was not one cow or ox in the field!

"By the great Jupiter," shouted Apollo. "Someone has stolen my cattle!" He raced across the field calling his cattle. But the rocks threw back the echo of his voice as though mocking him. No other sound except the singing of the birds could be heard.

"By my father who sits on high Olympus, the thief shall pay for this!" With this great oath, Apollo began to run down the mountain side. Suddenly he saw the marks of hoofs in the soft earth, and also the criss-cross print of some strange creature.

"What mark is this?" Apollo cried. "Surely no living creature has a foot like this! And the hoofprints of my cattle only lead to their own field, but I saw for myself that they are no longer there!" And Apollo walked slowly on down the mountain. His forehead was wrinkled with thought.

At the foot of the mountain he met the old man mending his fishing nets. The old man did not know that Apollo was a great god. He called out a greeting to the handsome stranger.

"Old man," Apollo replied, "have you seen any cattle passing this way?" The old man looked frightened, and only shook his head. But when Apollo smiled at him and seemed so friendly, he told him the wonderful and strange thing he had seen that night.

"It was a baby, a tiny baby," the old man

admitted. He hardly believed himself that what he said was true. "And he was driving a great herd of cattle *backwards!*"

Apollo shouted with rage, but he thanked the old man kindly before he raced on his way. It could be no other than his newborn brother. The great Jupiter had told him that very morning the news of Mercury's birth. Only the son of a god would be able to do such a deed when he was just a day old. How dared Mercury do such a thing!

When he reached the cave by the sea where Maia and her son, Mercury, slept, Apollo went up to his brother's cradle. Mercury lay with his little head on the pillow and his lyre was held tightly under one arm.

"Brother," Apollo cried, "what have you done with my cows and oxen?" Mercury opened his eyes very wide, and looked at Apollo.

"You woke me up," he said. Apollo paid no attention. He asked his question over again.

"Cows? Oxen?" Mercury said. "Brother, how should I know about such things? I was born only yesterday. I have never heard those words before. I could not have stolen them." Apollo was very angry.

"That is a lie!" he shouted. "You know where my cattle are." And he picked Mercury up out of his cradle and shook him as hard as he could. But Mercury only laughed. Then Apollo tried to tie his little fists together with a rope. But with a quick twist of his hands, Mercury slipped away. He picked up his lyre, and ran out of the cave.

"Mercury," Apollo called after him. "You shall be punished for this!" And he ran after his little brother, and made him come with him before their father, the great Jupiter.

Jupiter listened to all that Apollo told him about the disappearance of the cattle, and what the old man at the foot of the mountain had said. Then the great king asked Mercury to tell *his* story. Mercury saw that his father knew the truth. So he smiled and winked his eye. His father watched him, and laughed to himself, but he could not forget that Mercury had done a very naughty thing.

"You may have hidden your brother's cattle for a joke," Jupiter said, "but you should not have lied to him about it. Now it is right that your brother, Apollo, should punish you."

And then the great Jupiter turned to Apollo and said, "But remember, my son, it is good to be kind and forgiving to those who are yet young." Mercury heard this, but Apollo looked so angry that he was afraid. Then he remembered the lyre he had made. He took it from under his arm, and played on it and sang to his brother.

Apollo loved music. He had never seen or heard a lyre before, and he smiled with delight in spite of himself.

"You must give me that," he said to Mercury.

"But it's mine," Mercury cried. "I made it."

"But you must pay for stealing my cattle, and telling me that you did not. If you give me the lyre, and show me where you have hidden my cattle, I will forgive you."

Mercury looked down at his lyre. He ran his

fingers across the strings, and looked at his father.

"You must do what your brother asks," Jupiter said kindly, but firmly. Mercury handed the lyre to Apollo, and said that he would take him to his cattle.

"And do you promise never to do such a thing again?" Apollo asked. Mercury looked down at his toes, and nodded his head. He did not want Apollo to see the tears he was blinking back. He hated to give up his lyre. Apollo smiled.

"Then I will give you something to show that I have forgiven you," he said. And he handed him a magic wand. It was very beautiful with a tiny pair of wings on the end of it, and two gold snakes twisted around it.

Mercury thanked his brother, the great god of the sun, for his kindness. Then taking him by the hand, and clutching his new wand with the other, he led Apollo to the hidden valley. There were the beautiful cattle safely grazing in the fields.

The Hundred-eyed Argus

WHILE PROMETHEUS was chained to the rock at the end of the world, many people passed by. Some would stop and talk to the brave god who bore his torture with such courage. Some came especially to see him and bring comfort or ask for advice.

Once a winged chariot made all of green and gold flew near the great rock. It was full of beautiful mermaids. Their long hair was seaweed, and the wind blew it back from their faces. Tears of pity fell down their cheeks as they gazed up at Prometheus. They talked to him, and tried to comfort him, but there was little they could do.

So when the shadows of evening began to creep around the rock at the edge of the world, and the bright stars began to prick their way through the darkening sky, the mermaids climbed back into their carriage. Again the wings of green and gold began to flutter, and the chariot flew off into the dusk.

Once an old man with a beard of orange seaweed, and shiny scales on his chest, came riding by on a winged sea horse. Around and around the rock he flew, tugging at the reins. The sea horse tossed his head, and bucked, and flapped his wings, but at last he stopped in front of Prometheus. The old man was no other than Oceanus himself, god of the wide river, Ocean, which people then thought ran all around the world.

King Oceanus had come on a long, long journey. He wanted to do something to help Prometheus. But Prometheus only smiled sadly and shook his head. He must be patient and wait for the great hero who he knew was to come and free him. And the old king had to mount his winged sea horse and ride away on the pathway of silvery air, unable to help his brave friend.

But the strangest visitor of all was a white cow, a pure white cow with sad brown eyes.

She trotted a little way across the fields near the great rock, and stopped and turned her beautiful white head to look behind her and around her. Then she wandered on. Always she would look behind her, for following her was a strange black-haired monster who carried a shepherd's crook. He was covered with eyes — a hundred eyes!

He was the hundred-eyed Argus, sent by Juno, queen of the gods, to watch this beautiful white cow day and night. He never got tired, for he could sleep with two of his eyes at a time, and watch her with all his others. Never could the white cow escape from his sight!

Finally the cow looked up and saw the great figure of Prometheus chained to the rock with the cruel eagle hanging over him.

"What land is this?" said the white cow. "Who is the great man chained there on the rock?"

"Poor tired Io," said Prometheus gently. "Are you still wandering around the world?"

"Who called me Io? Who knows my name?" cried the white cow.

"I called you, fair Io. I am Prometheus, and I know much of what has been and what is to be."

Yes, Prometheus knew that this white cow was the once-beautiful maiden Io, who had been admired by the great Jupiter. Juno, his wife, had been very jealous. To make sure no harm would come to Io through Juno's jealous anger, Jupiter turned the lovely maiden into a pure white cow. He thought that in such a form Juno would not recognize her.

But Juno was very wise and she asked Jupiter to give her the beautiful white cow. Jupiter was afraid if he did not, Juno would guess the truth, so he gave her the cow.

Juno then called upon the hundred-eyed Argus to watch over her new pet. Never was he to take his eyes from the white cow. And so Io wandered from land to land. She always hoped that someone would rescue her from the terrible herdsman with the hundred eyes. Some of the eyes were green; some were black; some were blue. And all of them stared at her with a wicked gleam.

"Tell me, Prometheus, must I go on forever in the form of a cow? Will I never be able to be with my friends again? Will this hundred-eyed creature follow me forever?"

"Not forever, lovely Io," replied Prometheus. "And take comfort in this. Many hundreds of years from now one of your family, Hercules, will be a great hero. He will be the hero who will free me from these terrible bonds!"

The white cow sighed and lay down to rest on the sweet grass. Prometheus was indeed a friend and comforter for the unhappy Io. But near her as always, leaning on his crook, sat the Argus, blinking his hundred eyes.

Now Jupiter, on his throne on high Olympus, called his son Mercury, who had grown up to be the messenger of the gods.

"Mercury," he said. "I cannot bear seeing the beautiful Io followed by that terrible creature. I know it is almost impossible to surprise and kill a monster with a hundred eyes, but perhaps you could think of a way?"

"I'll see what I can do, Father," replied Mercury. He put on his shoes with little silver wings on the heels, and flew down to the rock where Prometheus was chained. There he played tunes on pipes made of reeds.

The hundred-eyed Argus smiled when he heard Mercury's sweet music. He did not know that this young man was one of the gods.

"Here is a pleasant place to sit, shepherd," the Argus called out to Mercury. "Come rest with me, and play on your pipes." Mercury came over and stretched out on the grass next to the Argus and the beautiful white cow.

"I can sing you songs of love and adventure," he said.

"Wonderful! Wonderful!" cried the Argus.

Mercury began to sing of the deeds of men and gods of long ago. He told of great battles, of dragons, of beautiful women. And in between he would play soft, sleepy music on his pipes. First one of the Argus's eyes closed, then another. Mercury sang on.

The lids of a few more of those hundred bright eyes grew heavy, and shut, and the Argus sighed a deep sigh. But always he managed to keep a few eyes open.

Mercury smiled. The music from his reed pipes drifted through the afternoon sunshine. The birds added their notes to the god's song, and the air was heavy with the sweetness of a summer day. At last only one gleaming eye remained open.

"There once was a gay young water nymph," sang Mercury as he watched the last wakeful eye. "And my foolish son Pan fell in love with her." His song told of the beautiful nymph running from Pan through fields of flowers, down to the lonely riverside. He sang of the river gently flowing over white rocks and mossy stones, and of the whispering of the trees and grass as they watched the lovely maiden's flight.

The Argus's eye was almost closed. Mercury sang more softly.

He sang of the water nymph being turned into a tuft of reeds — of Pan's sighing with sorrow — of the sweet song his sighs made in the reeds.

The Argus's last eye was shut! All hundred eyes were closed in sleep!

Quick as a flash Mercury jumped up. He drew out his long knife, and, with one stroke, cut off the hundred-eyed Argus's head! The beautiful white cow, Io, rose to her feet. At last she was free from the terrible herdsman; no longer would he follow her around the earth. Thanking Mercury with a look from her big soft brown eyes, Io trotted happily across the fields and away to another far-off part of the world.

Prometheus Unbound

THE HERO who Prometheus knew would rescue him from his terrible torture was Hercules. Hercules was a strong and brave young man whose father was one of the gods, and whose mother was a woman of the earth. This made him half man and half god, so that he was able to do things that the ordinary man of the earth could not do.

Juno, who was queen of the gods, took a great dislike to Hercules. She did not want the gods to marry women of the earth. So Juno did all she could to make the life of this son of a god and an earthly woman as difficult as possible.

In Mycenae, the land where Hercules lived, there was a wicked and cowardly king called Eurystheus. Juno gave this king the power to make Hercules his slave for twelve years. Eurystheus did not know that Hercules was half man and half god, but he did realize that this youth was much stronger and braver than other men. Eurystheus was afraid of young Hercules.

"I shall give him a task, and forbid him to return until he has accomplished it," Eurystheus said to one of his counselors. "It shall be such a task that he will never come back alive." And the wicked king chuckled with satisfaction.

Eurystheus had heard that in a beautiful garden somewhere in a far-off land there grew some golden apples. They were owned by maidens called the Hesperides.

"Get me those apples!" Eurystheus ordered Hercules. "And see that you do not come back without them!"

Hercules had no idea where the garden of the Hesperides was, and he wandered for many a day and night through many lands. But there didn't seem to be any garden with golden apples, and no one was able to tell him anything about it.

At last he came to the edge of the world. There, to his horror, Hercules saw a great man chained to a huge rock with an eagle cruelly attacking him. This seemed dreadful to Hercules, and with anger he placed a poisoned arrow in his bow, and lifting it, aimed·carefully.

Ping! The arrow whizzed through the air and struck right at the eagle's heart. With a great scream the bird flapped his wings helplessly, then fell headlong down past the edge of the earth, down into black space. Hercules climbed quickly up the side of the rock and began to break the chains around the man's wrists.

"Thank you, Hercules," the man said. "I have been waiting for you for a long time."

"How did you know who I was?" asked Hercules in surprise.

"I am Prometheus," the man replied. "My power to foresee many things told me that you would save me. If there is any way in which I can repay you, I will gladly do so."

"Perhaps you can tell me where I can find the garden of the golden apples."

"Have you ever heard of Atlas?" Prometheus asked. Hercules shook his head. "He is the father of the Hesperides," the god explained. "He might get the golden apples for you." Hercules leaned forward when he heard this. His spirits began to rise.

"Where can I find him?" he asked. Prometheus smiled, and told him to look over the edge of the world. Hercules lay down on his stomach and leaned over the edge of the world. There below him, with the whole world on his shoulders, stood a giant. The muscles in his arms bulged under its weight.

"Are you Atlas?" Hercules called down to him.

"Yes," the giant replied. "What do you want?"

Hercules told him his errand.

"I'll get the apples for you," Atlas said, "if you will hold the world for me while I am gone." Hercules agreed to this.

All the earth shook and the trees quivered as Atlas shifted the world onto the shoulders of Hercules. Then he set forth on his journey to visit his daughters, and get the golden apples from their garden.

He was gone a long time. The world got heavier and heavier. The shoulders of Hercules began to ache and his back bent under the weight, for he was not used to it the way Atlas had been. He began to think that Atlas would never return, and sometimes he was so tired he thought the world would slip and fall, whirling off into space.

Days passed and still the giant did not come back. There was nothing Hercules could do but continue to hold the world. There was no one around to help him. Soon every bone in his body ached.

Finally Atlas returned. He was not looking forward to taking the world back onto his shoulders. It was nice to feel so light and free. Hercules seemed to be holding the world up very well.

"I've got the apples," Atlas shouted down to Hercules. "Don't you want me to take them to Eurystheus?"

Now that Hercules knew how heavy the world was, he was not at all sure that Atlas would ever return and take back the burden.

However, he agreed, saying, "Won't you please hold the world a minute while I make a pad to ease my shoulders?"

Unsuspecting, Atlas replaced the world on his shoulders. Hercules quickly snatched the golden apples, and scrambling up on to the earth he took them to Eurystheus, leaving Atlas to hold the world forever.

Hercules Cleans the Augean Stables

HERCULES not only saved Prometheus from his terrible torture, but also did many other wondrous and daring deeds. For King Eurystheus hated Hercules and tried to think of the most dangerous and most impossible errands for him to do. The king thought he would be killed and never return.

But time after time Hercules *did* return. Finally Eurystheus thought of a different kind of task to give Hercules.

"Hercules," said the wicked king — and he smiled as he thought of the troubles the young man had ahead of him — "have you ever heard of the Augean stables?"

"No, Your Highness," replied Hercules.

"Augeas is the king of a far-off land called Elis. He has three thousand oxen whose stables have not been cleaned for thirty years. You must clean those stalls in one day. No one

45

can help you, and if you do not do it, you will lose your life!" The young hero's heart sank. It sounded like an impossible task, but he wasn't going to let the king know how he felt.

"Certainly, Your Highness," was all Hercules said, as he turned to leave for the land of Elis.

The Augean stables stood on a green and sunny hillside. They were barns built of stone with roofs of yellow straw. Hercules was dressed in the skin of a lion he had killed, and he wore leather sandals on his bare feet. He stood in one of the doorways and looked around.

The stalls were the biggest Hercules had ever seen. They were in two rows on both sides of the barn. The rows seemed to go on for miles and miles. A pitch-black ox stood in each stall, his knees deep in dirt. The oxen bellowed and tossed their heads and kicked at the wooden doors of their stalls. The sunlight coming in through the open doorway shone on the millions of specks of dust that filled the air. The specks got in his eyes and caught in his throat.

Thirty years of dust and dirt to clean out in one day! Already it was almost noontime. Hercules shook his head. But he wasn't going to give up without trying.

First he drove the black oxen out on the hillside to graze. One thousand, two thousand, three thousand stamped out of the barn. Then Hercules found an old shovel and broom in a corner, and started to clean one of the stalls.

The barn was hot and stuffy. Drops of sweat ran down his face and shoulders. His eyes were red from the dust, and his back ached. Finally he decided to go out and rest. He had only cleaned twelve of the thousands of stalls, and the god of the sun, Phoebus Apollo, had reached the highest point in the sky. Apollo would soon be driving his fiery chariot downward behind the mountains. Then night would come.

What could Hercules do? Would he ever get the Augean stables cleaned by nightfall? There was no fierce creature that Hercules was afraid to fight. There was no adventure too dangerous for him. But such courage and dar-

47

ing could not help him in this task. It would take more than one day for him to finish this work.

Hercules shook his head again and again. It looked as if the wicked king at last had thought of an impossible task. The young hero threw himself down on the grass by a rushing stream. It flowed from a spring at the top of the hill. Hercules drank the cold water and washed his hot face. He looked sadly at the black oxen walking over the peaceful hillside. Then he closed his eyes and tried to think.

"Caw! Caw!" called a black crow from an old stump near the barn.

"Caw-caw-caw!" came the answer from another on the yellow straw roof. And a third black crow flew silently through the sky. Two robins hopped near the edge of the stream looking for worms. A thrush sang a sad little song from the linden tree.

"Poor Hercules! The stables so dirty and the day half gone."

"Caw! Caw! Why doesn't he use his head instead of his hands?" cried the crow.

"And how would that help?" asked one of the robins. "I'd be glad to help by carrying twigs from the barn but I cannot carry much."

"If only we could do something," chirped the other robin.

"Poor Hercules! Poor Hercules!" sang the thrush.

"We know a way! We know," cawed the crows. "Water washes dirt away. The stream could wash the dirt away!"

"Wash the dirt away! Wash the dirt away!" chirped the robins happily.

"But how can you tell him?" asked the thrush. "He doesn't know our language." Then the stream began to gurgle and whisper and laugh, and leap up over the bank on which Hercules lay. Higher and higher the water rose, until it touched the hero's dusty foot, washing the dirt away.

Hercules sat up as he felt the cold water. He saw his foot was white and clean again in its leather sandal. Then he jumped to his feet.

"Water," he cried. "That's the answer!" And he raced down the hill to the Augean stables.

Soon he was back with his shovel, digging a ditch for the water to run through. With a joyful chuckle the stream rushed down it and into the dirty stables. The stream got bigger and bigger until it was like a great river roaring and swirling out of one stable, into the next. It carried away all the thirty years of dirt!

"Caw! Caw!" cheered the crows. The thrush sang sweetly, and the robins hopped happily around Hercules.

And before the god of the sun, Phoebus Apollo, had disappeared behind the purple mountains of the west, the black oxen were back in their stalls. But this time they were spotless, and smelled of the sweet waters of the stream.

Once again Hercules surprised wicked King Eurystheus, and returned, successful, from his task. The Augean stables had been cleaned in one day!

Pandora's Box

T HE GREAT Jupiter was troubled. The people on earth were growing strong and healthy. Soon they would be as strong as the gods, and they might even try to capture the golden city on high Olympus. This must never be. The great Jupiter tried to think of a way he could make sure that they would never grow to be so powerful.

Finally he thought of a plan. He commanded Vulcan, the blacksmith, to make a young girl. When Vulcan brought her up to the top of Olympus, all the gods and goddesses came to Jupiter's court to see her. Each of them gave her a gift. One gave her beauty; one gave her love; and another gave her courage. And they decided to call her Pandora, which means "the gift of all."

Pandora laughed and talked like any other girl, and also, like most of the people down on earth, she had a great curiosity. Jupiter knew this and he smiled as he slipped a little gold box into her hands. He told her to take good care of it and see that no one opened it. Then he sent her down the Milky Way to visit the people far below.

This was wonderful, Pandora thought, as she slid past the stars. She reached out and tried to catch them, but she was going so fast they slipped through her fingers. The wind blew back her golden hair, and her cheeks were bright with excitement.

"I'm going to like it down on the earth," she thought. "And it will be nice having friends who are human beings, not great and powerful like the gods and goddesses."

A great crowd of children, and older people too, ran to meet Pandora as she landed on earth at the bottom of the Milky Way. She seemed like a bright fairy dropping out of the sky.

"Isn't she beautiful!" one of them cried.

"What is your name?" another asked.

"Where did you come from?" they all wanted to know.

Pandora smiled and laughed and tried to

answer all their questions. The birds flew around her head and rested on her shoulders singing sweet songs of welcome. Then one boy saw the pretty box Pandora held in her hand. There were strange figures and designs carved all over it.

"What's that?" he asked.

"Something the great Jupiter gave me," said Pandora.

"The great Jupiter!" the people cried in wonder. "What's in it?"

"I don't know." Pandora looked down at the box she held so tightly. "Jupiter told me I must *never* open it," she explained.

"But why?"

"He didn't say," Pandora answered.

"How strange!" they all said. "Couldn't you take just one look inside? Maybe there are beautiful jewels in it."

Pandora held the box up to her ear, and shook it gently. There was only a faint fluttering sound. It couldn't be jewels. What could it be?

"Open it! Open it!" the crowd urged. Pandora knew she shouldn't open it, but just one peek wouldn't hurt — just one little peek! Jupiter would never know. She wouldn't take anything out of the box.

The children crowded around her. "Go ahead," they cried, and they pushed closer. So Pandora opened the box just a crack.

Whiff! Out of the box flew every kind of Trouble — Sickness, Greed, Envy, Hate, Revenge, and many others. These Troubles buzzed and flew so close to the heads of all the people that they had to cover their faces with their hands.

"Oh! Oh!" they screamed. "Close it!" Pandora slammed down the top as quickly as she could, but one of her fingers caught in the corner.

"Oh dear!" she wailed. "What have I done?" What would happen now that she had let these Troubles out into the world? Jupiter would know that she had disobeyed him and opened the box. (Pandora didn't know that this was just what the great king had hoped she would do!) "Oh dear!" she cried again.

Then she saw there was still a crack under the lid where her finger was. She peeked through it into the dark box and gasped with surprise.

"There is still something in there!" And Pandora quickly pulled out her finger and pushed down the lid.

"What was it?" asked a small girl.

"It was a beautiful fairy. She was dressed all in silver and was holding a sparkling wand."

"Open it, and let us see too," urged the others. But Pandora had learned her lesson.

"No. Never again," she said. She wasn't going to let any other Trouble fly out into the world, even if it did look like a beautiful fairy.

Then suddenly a soft sweet voice came from inside the box. "Pandora!" it called. "Pandora! Don't let me out. My name is Hope. You'll need me. Don't let me out."

Pandora's eyes opened wide with surprise and she held down the lid very hard.

"Get me a piece of strong string," she ordered. When it was brought to her, she tied it around the box and knotted the string many

times so that it couldn't possibly be opened.

"Now we will never lose Hope," Pandora said with a sigh of relief.

So even though Pandora's curiosity had let many Troubles out of the box and brought unhappiness into the world, the people still had Hope to comfort them.

The Flood

SO MANY Troubles had flown out of Pandora's box that they caused the people on the earth to quarrel and fight. They were so wicked that they even dared to call the great god Jupiter horrid names. This made the king very angry, and Jupiter decided he had to do something about it. So he spoke to his servants and ordered a great storm to be started. Jupiter armed himself with many thunderbolts and hurled them one by one with all his might on to the earth below.

Lightning flashed angrily through the great black, rolling clouds, and the forges of the blacksmith, Vulcan, shook the earth. The wicked men and women ran terrified over the quaking ground, but there was nowhere they could go to get away from the storm. All the leaves fell off the trees and soon even the trees fell down. Then the rain came, in great white sheets, and the rivers and seas began to rise until they covered the dry land, and there was a great flood.

There were two, however, a man and a woman, who had been good. The great Jupiter saw them and he led them to a high mountain called Parnassus. They sat on the top of this mountain, holding tightly to each other's hands, and watched the angry green waves dash on the rocks far below them. The waves made white foam that looked like soap bubbles.

After a long, long time the rain stopped and the sun came out bright and warm, and the water began to run back into the rivers and oceans. Everything was green and fresh.

"Isn't it beautiful?" cried the woman, who was called Pyrrha. She looked down with wonder from the top of Mount Parnassus at the country far below her.

"All the others have been drowned," said the man, whose name was Deucalion.

"I think that is because they were bad people."

"But it will be lonely," sighed Deucalion.

"Let's pray and ask the Oracle what we should do," suggested Pyrrha.

The Oracle was a prophet, a very wise spirit, who could tell men and women what the gods wanted them to do. Pyrrha and Deucalion knelt on top of the mountain and, raising their arms toward the sky, prayed.

Suddenly a voice, that seemed to come out of a soft cloud, said, "Throw the bones of your mother into the sea. Do as I say and you shall be rewarded."

"Did you hear that?" whispered Deucalion.

"Yes, but we can't do that," replied Pyrrha. "It is wrong to disturb the bones of the dead."

"That's true," said Deucalion, and he was puzzled. They sat with their chins in their hands and thought. Then Deucalion jumped up.

"I know," he cried. "The earth is our mother. Mother Earth! Wouldn't the stones be her bones?"

"Maybe you're right!" said Pyrrha, excitedly. "We can try it anyway." And hand in hand they raced down the mountain to the

seashore. The sand was very white, and there were many stones washed gently up on it by the waves.

Deucalion picked up a smooth white stone. He ran to the edge of the water and threw it out into the blue and white foaming sea. Lo and behold, up from the place where the stone had hit the water rose a tall strong man who walked toward them.

"Isn't he wonderful!" exclaimed Pyrrha in amazement, and she leaned down and chose a round rosy stone, and tossed it into the sea.

As the stone fell, a woman stepped out of a wave and came slowly and gracefully toward the shore. Soon there were many men and women standing on the sand, throwing stones into the sea. They were all good and beautiful, and they lived happily together on the new clean earth ever after.

Phaëthon's Folly

DOWN ON the earth there was a little
boy called Phaëthon. He was very handsome
with big brown eyes and golden hair. He was
very good at all kinds of games. He was so
much better than the other boys with whom he
played that they were jealous of him. Phaëthon
lived alone with his mother. His mother's name
was Clymene, and Phaëthon loved her more
than anyone else in the world. One day one
of his playmates began to tease him.

"You haven't any father," he said to Phaëthon. "We all have fathers, but you haven't."

"Yes I have," said Phaëthon. "And he's bigger than any of your fathers."

"I don't believe it," all the boys cried.
"Where is he?"

"He's up there." Phaëthon pointed to the
sun.

"How can he be up there?" the children
jeered.

"Because my father is the great god of the sun! My mother said so."

"You, the great sun god's son!" All the boys roared with laughter. "That's a good one! We don't believe you. You can't prove it." Phaëthon was angry. He stood up very straight to make himself look as tall as possible, and clenched his fists.

"It's true!" he shouted. "I'll prove it to you. You just wait." With that he ran home. His mother would tell him how he could prove it.

"Mother! Mother!" he cried. "Isn't my father god of the sun?"

Phaëthon's mother, Clymene, put down her sewing as her son ran in through the open doorway.

"Of course, Phaëthon. I have told you that many times."

"Well," said Phaëthon, all out of breath from running so fast. "The other boys don't believe me. How can I prove it?"

"Why don't you go up and ask your father?" his mother suggested with a smile. Phaëthon was terribly excited over this idea. He had never seen his father, who was so great a god. His father drove the chariot of the sun around the world. Not even the great Jupiter, who hurled the thunderbolts, could drive the flaming car of Day!

"Could I really, Mother?"

"Yes," replied Clymene. "But you must go alone."

"Can't I even take my puppy with me?" asked Phaëthon, beginning to be the least bit afraid.

"No, I'm afraid not. You must take along some food, though, for it is a long journey."

So Phaëthon started out, after giving his mother a kiss and his puppy a last loving pat. He walked and walked and walked. Finally he came to the foot of a sunbeam. Clymene had told him he was to climb up that sunbeam. The higher Phaëthon got, the hotter it grew. The little clouds that looked like powder puffs were floating far away in the blue sky. They didn't come near enough to give the tired boy any shade.

But Phaëthon wiped his brow with the big

white handkerchief that his mother had tucked in his pocket at the last minute, and climbed and climbed. Then he saw a doorway, but it was so hot and bright inside that he was blinded and dared not enter.

"Who's there?" asked a deep voice.

"Your son," answered Phaëthon, and his voice sounded very small.

"Welcome, my son!" And the god laid aside the beams that shone around his head so that his son could see to go in. Phaëthon was dazzled by what he saw.

The great god of the sun, his father, was dressed in rich purple robes, and sat on a throne that glittered with diamonds. Around him stood the goddesses of the Day, the Month, the Year, the Hours, and the Seasons. The god held his hands out to his son, and saw with pride what a fine boy he was.

"What do you want, Phaëthon?" he asked kindly.

"Please, dear Father — if you are my father, I should like some proof of it."

The god thought for a little, and then said

67

that he would grant any wish that Phaëthon might ask as proof that he was his son. Phaëthon was so excited and pleased when he heard this that he jumped up and down.

"Please, may I drive the chariot of the sun for just one day?" he asked, his eyes sparkling.

"No one but myself ever drives those horses that breathe fire from their mouths and nostrils and pull my chariot around the world," his father said sternly.

"But you promised, Father! You said anything I wished for proof," begged Phaëthon.

No god could take back a promise. His father knew this, but he was afraid for his young son. It took all the great god's strength to drive those horses, and he was a grown man. Phaëthon was only a boy.

"My son," he said, "you don't know what you ask. The first part of the way is steep, the middle is high up in the sky and you have to hold the horses in. You go past monsters, past the horns of the Bull, near the Lion's jaws, and where the Snakes writhe and twist. Make another wish, my son."

But Phaëthon was a stubborn boy. How proud he would be to tell his friends down on the earth that he, Phaëthon, had driven the chariot of the sun! Then they'd have to believe the god of the sun was his father!

At last the god gave in to his son and led him to the bright, beautiful chariot. Vulcan, the blacksmith of the gods, had made it. It was all of gold and silver, and the seat was lined with diamonds. The sun god rubbed a sweet-smelling ointment on his son's face so that the heat from the dazzling rays which he set on Phaëthon's head would not burn him.

As Dawn led the horses forth, Phaëthon jumped up on the diamond seat and, standing very straight, grasped the reins, and dashed out into the gray sky. All the stars rushed out of the way, and the goddess of the moon, Diana, ducked behind a great black mountain. All went well at first, but soon the horses felt how light the chariot was, and found the driver was not strong enough to control them.

They ran faster and faster, and left the well-traveled road. Twice they dashed so close to the earth that Phaëthon bounced about in the chariot. He tugged hard at the reins, but the horses paid no attention. Soon he noticed how hot it was and, looking down, he saw the world was on fire. The fiery breath of the horses had caught on the edge of the earth.

The seas were boiling, and the rivers began to dry up, and Mother Earth had great cracks in her face. The trees were charred, and the animals were running to get away from the flames that wrapped their tongues hungrily around all the beautiful plants.

Phaëthon was frightened. He tried hard not to cry, but big tears rolled out of his eyes. And Mother Earth called out to the great god Jupiter to help her.

Jupiter looked down from high Olympus, and saw the dreadful state of affairs. There was only one thing he could think of to do. He must hurl a lightning bolt at the young driver.

He didn't want to do this; so he called a meeting of all the gods to see if any of them could think of some better way to stop the fire. All the gods loved Phaëthon even though he

was a stubborn little boy; but they had to agree that it was the only thing to do.

So the great Jupiter threw a lightning bolt with all his might. It struck the chariot of the sun, and threw Phaëthon from his seat. He fell headlong, like a beautiful shooting star, into a great cool river. Then the king made a storm, and all the world was cooled with the rain.

Some people say that this fire made the Ethiopians black, and that the deserts don't have any trees because the flames came so close to that part of the earth. Who knows? But the sun god mourned for his little son, and vowed never again to let anyone else drive his fiery steeds.

Proserpina and the Pomegranate Seeds

T HE GREAT Jupiter had a sister called Ceres. Ceres was the goddess of planting and reaping, of the golden corn and the crimson poppies. She had a daughter named Proserpina whom she loved more than anyone else in the world.

One day when Ceres and Proserpina were walking through the fields, Proserpina cried: "Look at the morning-glories and the daisies." And she danced ahead of Ceres in the brilliant sunshine. "Smell the wild roses, Mother! See how the bees love them!"

After a while Ceres grew tired and sat down on a moss-covered rock under a tree on top of a hill.

"Run along, dear child," she said. "I shall rest here."

"I'll pick you some flowers," Proserpina answered gaily. And she sang to herself while she broke the bluebells and daisies carefully by the

73

stems as Ceres had taught her. That way she was sure not to pull them up by the roots. Soon she had a big bunch, but then she saw some marigolds growing in the marsh at the foot of the hill. How pretty they would be with the other flowers! She skipped down the bank and out of sight of her mother.

Suddenly, out of the bushes crashed a chariot drawn by pitch-black horses. A big man was standing in the chariot snapping his long whip over the backs of the horses. The ground shook under the pounding of their hoofs. Proserpina was so frightened she couldn't move. She had never seen anything like this before. She felt very small and helpless.

This strange dark man was Pluto, king of the Underworld. In those days, everyone who died went to the land of the Underworld. Around it flowed a deep black river; and an old, old boatman named Charon rowed everyone who came to Pluto's kingdom across this shadowy river. The Underworld was far below the earth, even farther below than the workshops of the blacksmith Vulcan.

Pluto stared at Proserpina with his great black eyes under his bushy eyebrows.

"How lovely she is!" he thought. "How nice it would be to take this child of the sunshine down to the dark Underworld with me."

And with that he cracked his whip and called out to his black horses as they galloped forward. Proserpina dropped her flowers, and started running back to her mother, but Pluto snatched her up into his arms.

"Come with me, my pretty child," he said with a chuckle.

"Mother! Mother!" Proserpina screamed. "Help! Mother! Help!"

But Pluto wouldn't listen to her cries. The horses rushed on over the fields with the chariot bumping over the uneven ground. Soon they came to a huge black hole which looked like a great mouth opening to swallow them. Into this pit they went, down and down, far under the earth to the dark palace of Pluto.

Ceres, resting on the hilltop, heard her daughter's cries and jumped to her feet, but she couldn't see anyone.

"Proserpina! Proserpina!" she called again and again, but there was no answer. Ceres was frantic with worry, and ran swiftly over the fields looking behind bushes and rocks for her little girl. Suddenly she saw the flowers, that Proserpina had gathered with such care, scattered over the ground.

"Someone has run off with my child," the poor mother wailed.

Day after day Ceres wandered over the earth asking everyone she met if he had seen little Proserpina.

That year the corn did not ripen and the poppies did not wave their crimson petals because Ceres wept over the loss of her daughter. She was so sad and weary that she finally went to her brother Jupiter, king of the gods.

"Help me, dear brother. Help me find my only daughter," begged the heartbroken mother. "Bring her back to me."

"Pluto, the king of the Underworld, took her away with him," replied the wise Jupiter. "If Proserpina has eaten any food that was given her in the Underworld there is little I can do to help you. The Fates will not allow anyone to return who has eaten below the earth."

While the great Jupiter was saying this, little Proserpina was sitting on a beautiful throne in the palace of Pluto. Many servants were waiting on her. But Proserpina was not happy.

"I want to go back to my mother," she cried. "It's so dark down here. Where is the sunshine?"

"You are a queen now," Pluto told her.

"I don't want to be a queen," Proserpina sobbed.

A little servant offered her some bright red fruit. "Taste one, my dear," said Pluto. "You must be hungry. These are called pomegranates."

Proserpina was hungry and they looked so good that she took one and bit into it.

"*Ummm!*" she said. But the pomegranate was so full of seeds that she found it hard to separate the sweet fruit from them, and so she did not eat it all.

Little did she know that because she had

eaten she would never be able to go back to her mother for good.

When news of this reached Ceres, she wept and wrung her hands.

"Oh, kind brother, is there nothing you can do?" she asked the great Jupiter.

Jupiter felt very sorry for his sister. Besides, he knew that unless Ceres was happy, there would be no harvest, and the men and women on the earth would starve. Maybe they could make a bargain with Pluto.

As long as Proserpina had only eaten part of the pomegranate, would Pluto let her come back to her mother for six months of the year? The other six months she could stay with him and be his queen. Even though Pluto wanted Proserpina forever, he could not harden himself against her mother's tears. At last he agreed.

So every year pretty Proserpina returns to the earth with the spring. All the trees and flowers begin to grow, and the birds begin to sing to tell the world that Proserpina has come home. All summer she plays in the fields with her mother, but in the autumn she must return to the Underworld. Then the leaves fall from the trees and the long winter begins. But Proserpina always comes back again, bringing the spring!

Perseus and the Gorgon's Head

THERE ONCE was a young hero called Perseus. Like the great Hercules, Perseus was the son of a god and an earthly woman. When he was born, the Oracle sent a message to the baby's grandfather, who was king of the land. It warned him that his grandson, Perseus, would be the cause of his death. For the gods knew that when Perseus grew up, he would accidentally kill his grandfather in a dart-throwing contest.

But the grandfather had no way of telling when or how this grandson would cause his death. He was frightened. What could he do? He walked back and forth on the marble floor of his room. How could he get rid of Perseus?

One dark and stormy night, when the wind shrieked and howled so that no other sounds could be heard, the grandfather and two of his strongest servants went into the little boy's room. They grabbed Perseus and his mother, the beautiful Danaë. The men then threw them, struggling and screaming, into a great chest. They tied a heavy rope around it, and the king locked it with a big black iron key. Then he commanded the servants to throw it into the angry sea. Surely now Perseus would die!

The waves washed the chest far out on the sea. First a wave would toss it way up out of the water, and then drop it deep down under another wave. Still another wave would pick it up and whirl it around and around. Perseus and Danaë were thrown from one side of the chest to the other.

Perseus held tightly to his mother, and tried hard not to show how frightened he was. Brave Danaë held him in her arms and told him stories. She pretended they were in a boat, traveling around the world. She told him of the strange and beautiful lands they would visit. And often it made Perseus forget they were locked in a wooden chest.

Then one day a great wave came along and

picked up the chest and dashed it with a crash on to the rocky shore of a far-off land. At first Perseus and his mother were frightened because they did not know what had happened. But when they no longer rocked and tipped or were thrown about, they realized that they were on dry land. How could they get out of the chest? They pushed and pushed, and pounded on the lid with their fists, but it would not open.

It happened that a fisherman was walking along the shore and came upon the chest. As he drew near he heard the pounding and muffled cries of Perseus and Danaë.

"What is this?" he said to himself in surprise.

Hearing the fisherman's voice, the two in the chest called louder, "Help! Help! Let us out!"

The fisherman pulled out a big knife, cut the rope, and broke open the lid. Out crawled the tired mother and her child. The two clung to each other shivering with the cold. The fisherman felt sorry for them and brought them to his small cottage not far from the shore.

There, for many years Perseus and Danaë stayed with the fisher folk. Perseus soon learned to be a good fisherman, and he and his mother lived happily together. But one day King Polydectes, proud ruler of this far-off land, happened to pass through the little fishing village.

Danaë was in front of the cottage picking a bunch of flowers when the king rode past. Polydectes thought she was very beautiful standing there, with the sunshine falling on her bright hair and her arms full of gay flowers. He stopped to talk to her and fell in love with her.

Polydectes did not know that Danaë had a son, and when he met Perseus, he was angry. Perseus did not like Polydectes either, and he knew that his mother did not love the proud king or want to marry him. But what could she do? No one dared say no to anything the king asked.

Since King Polydectes did not like Danaë's son he decided to get rid of him. He told Perseus he must bring him the head of a monster called Medusa. Now, Polydectes knew that only a god or goddess could do this and that no human being would be able to. He did not know that Perseus was the son of a god.

Perseus set out on this dangerous adventure. He knew he had to do something to keep his mother from marrying a man she hated. If he could return with Medusa's head, and surprise the wicked king, he was sure he would be able to save Danaë.

Medusa, he knew, was the name of one of the three monsters called Gorgons who lived in a cave somewhere near the sea. Once, Medusa had been a beautiful girl with long golden hair. She had been so proud of her hair that she had even dared to say that it was more beautiful than the shining locks of the wise goddess Minerva. This had made Minerva angry and she had punished the maiden by turning her into an ugly monster. Her golden ringlets had become hissing serpents!

Medusa was so terrible to look upon that no living thing could behold her without turning instantly into stone. All along the sides of her dark and gloomy cave stood stony men and animals who had looked at her face. Who was alive to tell where that cavern was? How could Perseus find it?

Perseus went to the great Oracle of the gods in Greece and asked its help. But even the Oracle could not tell him where he could find Medusa's home. It told him to go to the three witch sisters called the Graeae. They, too, lived in a cave, and they might be able to help him. So Perseus traveled for many miles till he came to the place where the Graeae lived.

As he entered he saw the three old sisters crouched together. They wore dark blue cloaks, and their faces were wrinkled with age. But the strangest thing about them was that they had only one eye among them. They sat in the middle of the cave rocking back and forth, and singing a strange sad song. First one old sister would slip the eye into her head and look around, then she would hand it to the next sister. And so they would pass the time, hour after hour, day after day.

Perseus crept up behind them. And as one old woman held out the eye to her sister, Per-

seus snatched it out of her hand! The three blind women were terrified when they found the eye was gone. They shrieked and screamed, and called upon the gods to help them.

"Who has stolen our eye? Give us back our eye!" they kept crying. "It is our only eye! We cannot see." And they clutched at the air with their bony fingers and blamed each other for keeping the eye. At last they heard a strange voice.

"I took your eye," Perseus said, "and I will not give it back to you until you tell me where I can find the terrible Medusa, and how I can cut off her head."

"Who are you?" The three old women cried out as they turned in the direction of his voice.

"I am Perseus," the voice said. "How can I kill Medusa? You must tell me, or you will never see again!" The three sisters put their heads together and began to whisper. Perseus watched them hopefully. But he could not hear what they were saying.

"Do not gaze upon her face or you will be turned to stone," they screamed at last.

"You must wear the magic helmet of Pluto, the god of the Underworld," said one sister. "When it is upon your head, you will be invisible."

"You must borrow the winged shoes of Mercury," said the second sister.

"You must ask Minerva to lend you her shield," said the third sister. And then they told him where he could find the terrible Medusa's cave. Perseus thanked them and gave back their eye. Then he went to pray to the gods for help.

The gods liked this brave young hero, Perseus, and they pitied him because he had to do such a dangerous deed. They were glad to lend him the things he needed.

Minerva gave him her bright silver shield.

"Use this shield of mine for a mirror. Always look in it," she told him. "Then you will never need to look at Medusa's face!"

The young messenger of the gods, Mercury, slipped off his winged shoes.

"Wear these," he said, "and you can fly swiftly above the head of the monster!"

And Pluto, himself, took off his magic helmet and placed it on the head of Perseus.

"Now Medusa will not be able to see you, but do not forget that she still can turn you to stone if you look at her," warned the god of the dark Underworld.

Then Perseus, with these three wonderful gifts of the gods, set out to find the cave of the Gorgons. He could spring up into the air, and fly swiftly through the clouds with the winged shoes on his feet. Perseus flew over sea and land. And, although the cave was at the very farthermost end of the earth, he reached it in only a few minutes!

He held the shield at arm's length, and looked up at it to see what he was coming to. The shield was a good mirror. In it he saw the cave. It was dark and covered with slime. Water trickled through the cracks in the wall and dripped over the people who had been turned to stone. Two of the Gorgons sat in gloomy silence, curled in one of the darkest corners of the cave. But the third Gorgon walked around and around the cave. She

moaned and cried aloud with grief and horror because she had lost her beauty. This was
Medusa! Her hair that had once been like a
shower of gold was a mass of twisting, squirm-
ing snakes.

Perseus was careful never to turn his head.
He was afraid that if he did he might look at
Medusa. At last the monster grew tired, and
lay down to rest.

This was the chance Perseus was waiting
for. He knew that because of the magic helmet he could not be seen, and he walked boldly
but quietly into the cave. He went up close to
Medusa, still careful to use Minerva's shield
as a mirror. Then, quick as a flash, he pulled
out his sword and cut off Medusa's terrible
head!

Perseus had carried out the most dangerous
part of the commands given him by King Polydectes. But he still had to bring the head to
the king without once looking at it. Even now
it could turn him to stone. So he held it high
up above his head and started on his way back
to his mother and the wicked king.

Perseus Saves Andromeda

THE NEXT day the dawn goddess, Aurora, gently parted the black curtains of night. She looked out and saw young Perseus flying back in the early sunlight over land and sea to rescue his mother. He was holding the horrible head of Medusa high in the air.

Just what made Perseus look down, he did not know. It seemed to him that he heard a strange sound. Was it a woman crying? Or was it just the gentle morning breeze? What he saw was a beautiful maiden chained to a cliff beside the sea.

She was dressed in a long white gown, and her dark hair fell softly over her shoulders. Tears slipped down her pale face as the cold waves washed over her bare feet. What a sad sight it was! Perseus started to fly down to her.

Then he remembered that this fair maiden must never see Medusa's head or she, like all the others, would be turned to stone. Quickly he dropped down on one of the cliffs out of her sight. He took off his cloak, and, always careful not to look at what he was doing, wrapped the snaky head in it and hung it on his belt. Now, no one could gaze upon the Gorgon's face. Now, he might be able to help the girl tied to the cliff. Perseus flew over to her.

"Why are you chained to this rock?" he asked.

The maiden was at first too shy to speak. Finally she said, "There is a horrible dragon that comes to our land. The Oracle says that if I am given to this dragon it will not come back any more to frighten our people." And with that she burst into tears. As soon as she finished speaking the water began to leap and splash round the rock.

Out of the green sea sprang a terrible dragon! He was covered with shiny black scales. His eyes were red and fire burst from his nostrils. His sharp white teeth shone in the sunlight. The maiden screamed and covered her face with trembling hands.

Perseus flew into the air from the rock where he was standing. With the help of the wings on his heels he hovered over the roaring dragon. He thrust his sharp sword between the scales around the dragon's neck. With a loud cry the monster sprang into the air, blood spurting from the wound. Again Perseus plunged the sword between the black scales. And again! And again! The water was red with blood. The air rang with the fearful cries of the dragon. Finally, Perseus struck the monster over the head with all his strength. The beast writhed and twisted, and with a gasp sank into the ocean.

"You have saved my life!" cried the beautiful young girl. She told him that her name was Andromeda. "How can I thank you?" she asked.

Perseus kissed her and begged her to marry him. That was all the thanks he asked. So they joyfully went back to Andromeda's palace.

94

Her mother and father were very happy and grateful to have their daughter safe again. A great feast was prepared to celebrate the wedding and there was much singing and dancing.

However, before Andromeda had been chained to the rock a man named Phineus had wanted to marry her. He had given her up when he learned that she was to be sacrificed to the terrible dragon. He was not very brave, and he was afraid to try to save her. But when he heard that Perseus had killed the dragon and that Andromeda was safe, he still wanted her for his wife.

He gathered together all the men in his court and they rushed to Andromeda's palace and into the wedding feast. Phineus tried to carry Andromeda away with him. But Perseus and the servants in the palace bravely fought them off. The banquet hall was in an uproar. The women screamed and the men shouted. The clash of swords and shields rang through the palace. Phineus had many more men on his side than Perseus. It looked as though he would win, and would take Andromeda away. Then

Perseus thought of Medusa's head that was still in the cloak fastened to his belt.

Springing into the air, he floated over the crowd. He unwrapped the head and held it up.

"Turn away your faces, my friends!" he shouted. And those who were faithful to Perseus turned aside their faces wondering what he could mean. But Phineus and his followers looked up angrily. Phineus was about to throw a spear at Perseus when his eyes fell on Medusa's face. That very second, while his arm was lifted, he was turned into stone. Another man started to call out. With his mouth still open, the words not yet spoken, he became another stone statue in the banquet hall. And so the enemies of Perseus still stand in the old palace, frozen forever just as they were when they looked at Medusa's head.

Perseus wanted to get back to his own land, and to his mother. This time he made up his mind nothing should stop him on his way. He quickly said good-by to Andromeda's grateful family and friends, and with his young bride started home.

It would be hard to describe Danaë's joy at seeing her son again and meeting the beautiful Andromeda. She put her arms around Perseus, and tears of joy ran down her cheeks. She told him how much King Polydectes wanted to marry her. She did not think she would dare say no to him any longer.

"I will take care of that, Mother dear," laughed Perseus. He left Danaë with Andromeda, and went to the throneroom of Polydectes. He walked boldly in, and stood before the king.

Polydectes jumped up when he saw who it was.

"You!" the king cried. "What are you doing here?"

"I have come back from my trip to Medusa's cave."

"But where is the head?" asked the king, not believing that Perseus had ever really been there.

"Right here!" replied Perseus, and he held the head before the king's eyes. Like all the others, the wicked king was turned to stone.

Perseus then returned his magic helmet and shield and winged shoes to Pluto, Minerva and Mercury. All the gods seemed very pleased that he had done so well. The wise goddess Minerva took the head of Medusa and placed it in her shield so it could no longer do anyone any harm. Perseus was glad to be rid of the terrible head at last, and he and Andromeda lived happily ever after.

The Big and the Little Bear

ARCADIA IS one of the most beautiful places in Greece. It is covered with rich green forests full of wild animals. The people who live in those forests today often tell the story of a beautiful woman called Callisto and her son, Arcas, who used to love to hunt.

They say that one day the great Jupiter, looking down from high Olympus, saw Callisto and her young son Arcas racing along the woodland paths after a stag.

"How beautiful she is! How graceful she is! I don't know when I've seen so beautiful a woman on earth," the great king said to Juno, his wife.

Juno did not like to have Jupiter admire any other woman.

"She is just a woman of the earth," she said scornfully. The great Jupiter thoughtfully smoothed his beard with his hand. He did not seem to hear what Juno said.

"She is almost as beautiful as a goddess," he said.

This made Juno really angry. Soon he would be saying that Callisto was as beautiful as she, queen of the gods. The more she thought about it the more jealous she became. Finally she decided that she could not let Jupiter see Callisto again.

But how could she prevent it? Jupiter was king of the gods and he could do anything he wished. Juno thought for a long time, and at last she decided on a plan. She waited until one day when Callisto was hunting alone in the forest. Then — quick as a flash — she changed the beautiful woman into a great black bear!

Callisto, who used to love to hunt, now had to run from the hunters. Forgetting that she herself was a wild beast, she fled from the other wild animals too. She was afraid to try to make friends with other black bears, so she wandered alone through the dark forests. The little animals whom she did not fear, like the squirrels and chipmunks, were afraid of her. How lonely she was!

Then one day Callisto saw a young hunter running through the forest. It was Arcas, her own dear son! She tried to call out to him, but she could only growl. So, running toward him with joy, she threw her huge furry arms around him. Arcas did not know that this black bear was his mother. He thought she was trying to kill him, and lifted his hunting spear to protect himself.

Just at this moment the great Jupiter looked down from high Olympus and saw what was about to happen. How dreadful it would be to have Callisto killed by her own son! As quickly as Juno had turned the beautiful Callisto into a bear, Jupiter turned Arcas into a bear too and placed them both safely among the stars in the sky.

Juno was very angry when she saw what the great Jupiter had done. The queen of the gods called to Oceanus, god of all the waters, who had brought her up.

"See what Jupiter has done!" Juno cried

furiously. "I changed Callisto from a woman to a bear and now Jupiter has placed her and her hateful son among the stars. I would rather have her still be a beautiful woman than receive such an honor. It is not fair! O Oceanus, please do something to help me!"

"They shall never rest beneath the Ocean as the other stars do. That shall be their punishment," replied the aged Oceanus, to please Juno.

And so any clear night if you look up toward the Milky Way, you'll see two groups of bright stars that, night after night, move round and round the world, but never sink beneath the Ocean to rest. They are called the Great and Little Bear, but you and I know they are really the beautiful Callisto and her son, Arcas.

How the Kingfisher Came to Be

ONCE UPON a time there was a king called Ceyx. Ceyx had a lovely queen whose name was Halcyone and they reigned happily together over their prosperous kingdom. But one day Ceyx's brother died. He hadn't had a day of sickness, and there didn't seem to be any cause for his sudden death. Ceyx felt that in some way his family must have made the gods very angry.

"It's the only explanation, my dear Halcyone," he said sadly to his wife. "I am going to sail to the far land of Claros and consult the Oracle of the gods."

"Don't go, dear husband," begged Halcyone. She was daughter of the god of winds and she knew how dreadful and dangerous was a storm at sea. "I am sure the gods could have no reason to be angry with us."

But Ceyx felt that he could never rest in peace until he had consulted the wishes of the gods by means of the great Oracle. So, after kissing Halcyone good-by, he set sail.

Soon after he lost sight of land, the winds began to blow and the rain began to fall. Ceyx's ship was dashed against the rocks, and the young king was drowned. His last prayer was that the waves might wash his body where Halcyone would find it.

Halcyone sadly waited and waited for her husband's return. As the days went by she grew more and more anxious, and burned incense to Juno, the wife of the great Jupiter, and queen of the gods. Juno felt very sorry for Halcyone and could not bear to have her pray for the return of one already dead. So the queen of the gods called her special messenger, Iris.

"Go down to Somnus, god of sleep," she commanded; "ask him to send the ghost of Ceyx to this unhappy Halcyone to tell her, himself, of his death."

Iris put on her rainbow robe for which she was so famous, and prepared to go to the gloomy cave where Somnus lived. She only dared to go because Juno had sent her. Even

Phoebus Apollo, the great god of the sun, never dared to look into the dwelling of the god of sleep.

Only a faint glimmer of light ever crept into the shadowy cave, and clouds gathered together in the dark corners. No rooster ever crowed to welcome the dawn; no watchdog ever howled to break the silence. Nobody dared to speak. There was no wind to rustle dry ieaves. There was no gate at the entrance to creak on rusty hinges. Only crimson poppies, the flowers of sleep, grew in front of the open mouth of the cave. At the bottom of the cave a great river flowed and its drowsy song put the god to sleep.

In the middle of the cave the god Somnus lay on a couch of black wood decorated with fluffy black plumes and black curtains. Drifting and whispering around him were dreams, all kinds of dreams: happy dreams, sad dreams, gay dreams, funny dreams and even nightmares.

Bright Iris rushed into the cave, lighting it up so that the god Somnus had to waken. She brushed the dreams aside so that her radiance spread around the black bed.

Stretching and yawning Somnus asked sleepily what she wanted. Quickly Iris explained about Ceyx and Halcyone, for fear she might fall asleep before she could win the god's help. Somnus was too sleepy to protest, and he agreed to send the ghost of Ceyx to Halcyone. Then he fell back onto his soft pillows and Iris sped back to Juno on high Olympus.

Halcyone was startled that same night by seeing the ghost of Ceyx standing before her. Now at last she knew that he had been drowned, and was determined to set out to find his body.

"Oh, my dear husband," she wept. "I knew this would happen!"

She prayed to Juno to help her. Day after day Halcyone wandered along the seashore, over white sands and up steep gray cliffs. All the time the angry green waves beat on the shore sending up foamy white spray. . . . *Boom! Boom!* . . . Sometimes they sounded like thunder, and sometimes they seemed to be roaring at her.

Finally one day when Halcyone was standing on top of one of the cliffs she saw the body of her husband on the waves far below. Weeping with joy, she leaped from the cliff to join Ceyx, and — lo and behold — she was changed into a bird, pouring forth a song of love and grief. Kind Juno changed Ceyx into a bird, too, so that he could fly over the water after Halcyone, and they could be together for ever and ever.

Today they are called the kingfisher birds. So whenever you see a kingfisher you must think of this story.

And for seven days before and seven days after the winter, the great Jupiter forbids the winds to blow. Then Halcyone sits on her eggs in her nest and sailors know that they can travel safely on the sea. Those are "halcyon days."

The Miraculous Pitcher

ONE DAY Jupiter thought he would like a change from life with the gods on Olympus, so he and Mercury set out for earth. Swiftly they raced through the clouds and soon were standing on a long winding road. The two gods, dressed like travelers, gathered their heavy cloaks about them and started on their way through the land.

As evening drew near, Jupiter and Mercury came to a village. Dogs barked at the two strangers as they walked through the streets. Children screamed at them and threw stones at their feet.

"This isn't a very pleasant welcome," remarked the great Jupiter.

"Perhaps it is only that the children and dogs have not been brought up well," suggested Mercury.

Soon they came to a beautiful house with bright light streaming out of the windows.

Jupiter and Mercury were tired and hungry, and knocked on the door to ask for food and shelter. A richly dressed servant opened the door and looked at them with a frown on his face.

"What do you want?" he asked crossly.

"We are strangers in this part of the land, and we are looking for a place to eat, and to rest for the night," Jupiter explained.

"We have no place for strangers," the servant answered. "Besides my master is giving a great feast tonight, and we have no time for people like you!"

"But could we not have a few scraps from the table if we waited in the kitchen?" asked Mercury. But the servant had already slammed the door in their faces.

The two gods said nothing as they went on to the next house. It, too, was a beautiful house with marble steps leading up to the front door; laughter and singing came from inside. Again they knocked and asked for a place to rest. And again they were turned into the street. So they passed from door to door with never a welcoming smile or kind word given them.

"These men and women of the earth seem to be like their children who threw stones at us," said Mercury. Jupiter only shook his head in grim silence. The light in his eyes and the frown on his face made Mercury think of the terrible lightning and thunder that shook the earth when the great king was angry.

Soon they came to the end of the village, and started to climb a rocky road that led to the top of a hill. They saw a faint light ahead of them. It came from the window of a tiny cottage with a roof of straw. Part of the window was patched with an old rag, and a faint thread of smoke came out of the chimney and twisted up into the darkening sky. As the two gods walked up the narrow well-kept path, they heard voices.

"Are you warm enough, my dear?" asked a deep voice.

And then they heard a woman's voice. It was sweet and shook a little. "Yes, thank you, husband."

"How I wish I could have brought you something from the village today, but our neighbors do not care to hear about our troubles or even to lend an honest man a warm blanket." And the gods heard a heavy sigh. They looked at each other, and then called out. The cottage door opened, and a bent old man with a long white beard stood before them. Jupiter explained that they were strangers without a place to stay for the night.

"Come in! Come in!" cried the old man and he held the door wide open. "We are poor folk and haven't much to offer, but all we have is yours." The gods smiled, and bent their heads to enter the low doorway.

"Baucis, Baucis," called the old man to his wife, "we have guests!" An old woman with white hair came from the fireplace. She curtsied to the strangers. Then the old man told them that his name was Philemon. The two lived alone on the hill. They didn't have any servants or a feast to lay before their guests, but they gave the best they had.

Baucis stirred up the fire, and put some herbs that Philemon brought from their tiny garden in a pot to cook. She covered the rough bench with a mattress stuffed with seaweed, and threw the only cloth they had in the cottage over it for the strangers to sit on. One leg of the table was shorter than the others. Philemon helped his wife stick a piece of slate under it to make it steady. As the old man stood up, his face was red from bending down. Baucis turned to the gods.

"My eyes are not as good as they once were, and so Philemon sees things for me. With him I have no need for eyes."

Philemon smiled. "My ears are not as good as they once were," he said, "but Baucis hears all that I need to hear." And the two old people looked lovingly at each other.

Then Baucis rubbed the top of the table with sweet-smelling oils. She filled a pitcher with wine, and placed a bowl of olives and radishes on the table. She put the stew she had made in big clay bowls, and served with it cheese, and eggs. Philemon said that he wished they could offer them more. But the gods told him that it was plenty and seemed like a feast to them after their long day's journey.

The gods kept passing back their cups for more wine, and Philemon poured it with fear that it would soon be gone. The pitcher was not very big, and it held all the wine they had. After a while it seemed strange to Philemon that there should still be plenty in the pitcher. He had filled the cups again and again. Wondering, he looked into it.

"Truly," he said to himself in great surprise, "it must be that my eyes are failing me like those of my poor wife." Out of the bottom of the pitcher bubbled a fountain of sweet red wine. How could this miracle be?

Filled with wonder he looked at the two strangers. Mercury was smiling, and Jupiter's eyes twinkled. Suddenly Philemon realized that the two strangers could be none but great gods.

"Baucis! Baucis! . . ." He whispered to his wife — and they fell on their knees before their guests.

"Forgive us," cried poor Philemon, "for offering you such poor food. We did not know who you were."

"We know that it was the best you had," said Jupiter kindly. "It is more than your neighbors in the valley offered us. You shall be rewarded for your hospitality!"

But Philemon and Baucis tried to think of a way they could honor the gods. Then they remembered the old goose who had been their pet for many years. He would make a fine feast for their noble guests.

But the goose was too quick for these old people. He flapped his wings and ran out of reach, and finally hid behind Jupiter and Mercury.

"Do not kill your goose," said Mercury. "We have had plenty to eat. Now all we ask is to rest under your roof until morning."

The next morning the great Jupiter and his son Mercury led the old couple to the top of the hill above their cottage. When Philemon and Baucis turned to look behind them at the valley below, they gasped with surprise. The valley was no longer filled with beautiful houses. It was a clear lake that looked like a mirror. In it they could see the white clouds in the sky. Their little cottage was the only building left standing.

And before their very eyes Philemon and Baucis saw their home turning into a beautiful temple. The wooden logs turned into pillars of marble, and the straw roof turned into gold. Carvings and decorations grew out of the corners, and the birds from all around came to sing on the roof. Old Philemon and Baucis stood there holding tightly to each other's hand, unable to speak.

"The wicked people of the valley have received their punishment," said the great Jupiter. "Now you shall receive your reward. You may have any wish you ask for." Philemon and Baucis looked at one another, and talked together for a few minutes. Then Philemon spoke to the gods.

"Our wish, O great gods from High Olympus," the old man said slowly, "is that we may never be separated, and may live the rest of our lives together. Neither of us wishes to live without the other."

Mercury and Jupiter smiled. They were glad to grant such a wish to the faithful and honest couple. Then the two gods said good-by and left them to care for the beautiful temple.

For many many years Philemon and Baucis guarded the temple that had once been their tiny cottage. Then one day, when they were both very, very old, they stood arm in arm in front of the marble pillars. They looked at the sparkling lake in the valley below, and at the green hillside around them. They listened to the songs of the birds, and they told each other how lucky and happy they had been. As they talked, Baucis looked at her husband and saw a crown of leaves around his head. She looked down at her own arms and saw that they were turning into graceful branches.

"Our time has come, husband," she said softly. "The gods have kept their promise." And so Philemon and Baucis were turned into two beautiful trees that grew out of the same trunk.

Some say that, even today, if you know where to find that little temple on the hillside, you will see a graceful linden tree and a great oak growing out of the same trunk. And if you listen carefully when the wind blows, you can hear Philemon and Baucis whispering together.

The Winged Horse

IN A far-off land called Lycia, there was once a monster whom the people called the Chimera. The Chimera was the most dreadful creature that had ever been known to walk the earth. Night after night he would creep into the towns and villages and kill any man, woman, or child who happened to be out in the streets.

There was no one alive who had seen the monster, although many had heard his terrible cries. Those who had been brave enough to lie in wait for him at night had never lived to tell what happened. All that could be found in the morning were broken spears and shields on the bloodstained ground. And there were strange marks of long sharp claws in the mud.

When Iobates, king of Lycia, heard of the Chimera, he ordered his guardsmen to hunt down this dangerous monster. But the guardsmen were too frightened. They told the king they would rather receive any kind of punishment than hunt the Chimera. King Iobates didn't know what to do. Somehow, he must save his people from that horrible creature.

Then one day a young stranger came to the court, and asked to see the king. He was very tall and handsome, and he was dressed like a soldier. He knelt before King Iobates and told him his name was Bellerophon.

"Where have you come from?" asked the king. "And what is your business here?" Bellerophon pulled a letter from his pocket and handed it to the king. The letter was from the king's son who lived in a distant kingdom. It was stamped with a big seal of red and gold. King Iobates broke it open, wondering what his son had to say about this young man.

The letter said that Bellerophon was a great hero. It was full of praise for the many brave deeds that he had done. But in the end it asked King Iobates to put him to death, for the king's son was afraid of Bellerophon.

King Iobates frowned, and rubbed his forehead. Bellerophon was such a fine young man.

However, his son must have had a good reason for writing such a letter. The king looked thoughtfully at Bellerophon, who was kneeling so politely before him.

"My son says you are very brave," he said slowly. "Have you heard of the Chimera who has brought such terror into my kingdom? Would you dare try to hunt him down? If you could kill this monster you would bring great relief and happiness to my people."

To the king's surprise, Bellerophon agreed to go after the monster. The king promised him a reward if he returned, but he didn't really think Bellerophon would ever come back.

Bellerophon had heard many tales about the terrible Chimera. He knew that only with the help of the gods would he ever be able to kill such a monster. So, like many other heroes, he went to ask the advice of the great Oracle.

The Oracle told him that there was a winged horse called Pegasus. It had sprung from the blood of Medusa when Perseus had cut off her head with its snaky hair.

"Ride the winged horse," said the Oracle,

"and you will be able to kill the Chimera."

But Pegasus was a wild horse, and no man had ever been able to ride him. Bellerophon was puzzled. How could he tame the wild Pegasus and where could he find him?

By this time the evening stars were shining brightly, and nothing could be done till morning. Bellerophon decided to sleep that night in the beautiful temple of the Oracle. He stretched out on the cool marble floor. The temple was dark and silent, and Bellerophon could hear the chirping of the crickets in the grass outside. He closed his eyes and tried to sleep.

Suddenly the room was filled with bright light. There, before him, was a goddess with golden hair and big gray eyes, and in her hand she held a golden bridle. It was the wise Minerva. Bellerophon was too surprised to speak.

"Bellerophon," said the goddess. Her voice rang through the temple like music. "You must ride the wild horse Pegasus. Take this magic golden bridle and come with me."

Minerva floated out of the temple and across

the dark fields. Bellerophon followed her full of wonder. She seemed like a beautiful warm light that made the goddess of the moon, Diana, cold and dim. Finally, Minerva stopped.

"Wait here," she said, and disappeared into the dark night as suddenly as she had come. After his eyes had become used to the soft light of the moon, Bellerophon saw he was standing near a clear pool of water. Then he heard a rustle in the bushes. A pure white horse stepped out of the woods and bent his graceful head to drink. His smooth coat shone in the moonlight, and out of his back grew two huge silver wings. This was the wild Pegasus!

Bellerophon hardly dared to breathe for fear he'd frighten Pegasus away. How was he going to slip Minerva's bridle over this horse's head? Perhaps he could creep up behind him, and leap on his back. Softly Bellerophon started to move toward the winged horse. He hid the bright bridle behind him.

Pegasus snorted, and raised his head. When he saw Bellerophon, he sprang into the air. He spread his great silver wings, and swept

in wide circles through the starlit sky. Around and around he went. Bellerophon's heart sank as he watched the birdlike creature flying up and up into the sky. Gone was the wild horse that would have helped him kill the Chimera!

But wasn't he flying a little more slowly? Wasn't he coming a little closer, drifting soundlessly down and down? Bellerophon held his breath as Pegasus sailed out of the sky, and stood again at the edge of the pool.

This time Bellerophon knew he must get the bridle over the horse's head. Surely Minerva's bridle must have some strange power. He looked at it in his hands shining in the moonlight. And he held it out, and whistled as he walked toward Pegasus.

Again the winged horse sprang into the air, but when he saw the golden bridle, he stopped. Then, lo and behold, he turned, alighted and walked to meet Bellerophon. He pushed his soft, quivering nose into the bridle as though he knew this hero was to be his master.

Quickly Bellerophon leaped on his back and settled himself between the silver wings. Away

127

they flew high up in the air, sailing over the moon and around the stars. At first Pegasus bucked and tossed his mane and kicked at the air. He had never had anyone on his back before. Bellerophon had to hold on tight and press his knees close to the horse's sides. But soon Pegasus got used to his rider and his golden bridle.

It did not take them long after daybreak to find the Chimera. They were flying so high in the sky that it was easy to see things down on the earth.

The great monster was wandering around his den in the forest. Bellerophon had never seen such a beast. He was neither dragon nor serpent. His head looked like a lion's, but his neck was like a goat's. And his back was all covered with scales with sharp spears on his tail. When he slashed it around it cut great chunks out of the trees! He roared at the birds, who flew with frightened cries to the treetops. Fire burst from his mouth, scorching and blackening the ground. The white bones of his victims were crushed and scattered around him.

But Bellerophon wasn't afraid. With a soft word to Pegasus, he swooped down on the monster. They had to move swiftly to escape the flames from his jaws. Bellerophon drew his sword and plunged it into the Chimera's scaly back. The monster lashed his tail as black blood spurted from the wound. He snorted and roared and leaped into the air, but already Pegasus had carried Bellerophon far out of his reach.

Once again Pegasus swooped down, and Bellerophon struck the angry monster. Once again the monster sprang upward with wild cries that people, trembling with fright, heard for miles around.

The third time was the last. Bellerophon, clinging tightly to the neck of Pegasus with one arm, leaned way down and thrust his sword into the Chimera's throat. The horrible creature turned and thrashed about, then fell upon the ground with such a thud that the whole earth trembled. The terrible Chimera was dead!

No longer did the men and women of Lycia have to shut themselves up in their houses as soon as night began to fall. No longer were the guardsmen afraid to watch the city gates at night. And King Iobates was so pleased and grateful to Bellerophon for killing the Chimera that he gave the brave young man a wonderful palace to live in and his own beautiful daughter for a wife.

For many years after, Bellerophon rode Pegasus each day, flying up into the blue sky —higher and higher—until only the flashing of the horse's silver wings could be seen from the earth below.

Index of Names and How to Pronounce Them

131